Hansel
and
Gretel

This book belongs to

Age---------

This edition first published in 2014 by Milly&Flynn®
an imprint of Ginger Fox Ltd
Stirling House, College Road, Cheltenham GL53 7HY
United Kingdom

www.millyandflynn.com
www.gingerfox.co.uk

Copyright © 2013 Ginger Fox Ltd

Retold by Nina Filipek
Illustrated by Jacqueline East

ISBN: 978-1-909290-11-2

10 9 8 7 6 5 4 3 2 1

Printed and bound in China.

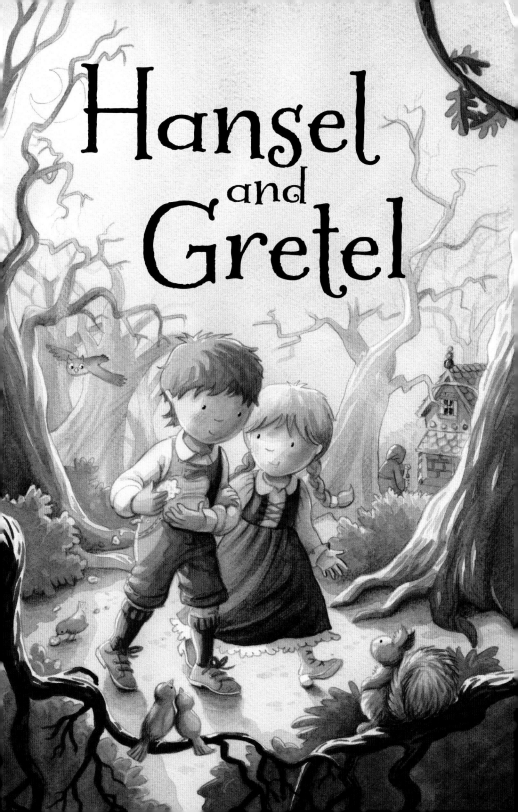

Hansel
and
Gretel

Once upon a time there was a boy called
Hansel and a girl called Gretel.

They lived with their father, who was a
poor woodcutter, and their cruel stepmother.
Often they went to bed hungry.

One night, they heard
their stepmother say,

"We have only enough food
for ourselves. Tomorrow we will
have to take the children into the
woods and leave them there."

7

Gretel cried and cried,
but Hansel had a plan.

"Don't worry," he said to Gretel.
"I will look after you."

Once everyone was asleep, Hansel
crept outside and filled his pockets
with white pebbles. Then he went
back to bed.

The next day,
their stepmother and father
took them into the woods.
Hansel stayed back, and as they
walked along, he dropped the
pebbles onto the path.

When they were in the
middle of the woods, their
father made a big fire.

Their stepmother told them
that she and their father
were going to collect
more wood. She told the
children they would come
back for them later.

But they did not come back.

Gretel began to cry.

Hansel said, "Don't worry.
When the moon comes out we
will find our way home."

At last the moon came out, and the white pebbles shone brightly in the moonlight. Hansel and Gretel followed the trail of pebbles all the way back home!

When their father saw them he was so pleased.

Their stepmother,
however, was not happy.
That night, they heard her say,

"Tomorrow we will have
to take the children deeper
into the woods and leave
them there."

When everyone was asleep, Hansel crept downstairs to get some more pebbles, but this time the door was locked.

He went back to bed empty-handed and very sad.

The next day, their stepmother woke them up early.

She gave them each a piece of bread.
Then she took them deep into the woods.

As they walked along, Hansel
dropped crumbs of bread onto the
path behind them.

They reached the deepest part of the woods, where their stepmother told them to wait. She said she would come back for them later. Hansel and Gretel waited, but she did not come back.

Gretel shared her bread with Hansel, and soon it grew dark.

Hansel said, "Don't worry. When the moon comes out we will follow the trail of breadcrumbs home."

At last, the moon came out. But Hansel and Gretel could not see the breadcrumbs.

The hungry birds had eaten them all!

Hansel and Gretel were lost in the woods, and spent the night huddled together. The next day when they awoke, they saw a white bird singing in a tree. It had such a lovely call that they followed it. The white bird led them to the strangest cottage.

They could not believe their eyes! The cottage was made of gingerbread and sweets of every kind.

The children were so hungry that they broke off sweets to eat, and failed to notice the old woman watching them.

The cottage door opened
and the old woman came out.

She invited them inside and gave them pancake
but she was only pretending to be nice.

Really she was a wicked witch

The **wicked witch** locked Hansel in a cage, and she made Gretel scrub the floor.

very day the **wicked witch** fed Hansel
ige meals. She was fattening
m up to eat him!

21

So Hansel played a trick on her!

When she reached in the cage to feel how fat he was, he stuck out a chicken bone.

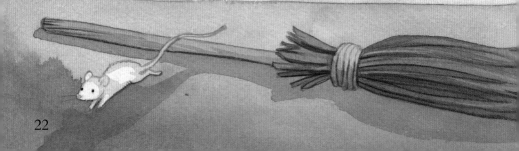

The **wicked witch** had bad eyesight – so she thought it was his finger. She was disappointed that he was not getting any fatter.

One day, the **wicked witch** decided to eat
Hansel anyway – even if he was too thin.
She told Gretel to get into the oven to
check that it was hot enough. She was
really planning to eat Gretel as well!

Clever Gretel pretended she did not know how.
So the wicked witch said she would show her.
Gretel saw her chance. She shoved the
wicked witch inside the oven and
quickly locked the door.

Then she freed Hansel from the cage.

Hansel and Gretel found some precious pearls in the wicked witch's house.

"These are better than pebbles!" said Hansel. "We can take them back for father." So he put some pearls in his pocket.

They left the cottage and at last they found the path home.

Their father was overjoyed to see them
again, and told them that their stepmother
had died while they were gone.

Hansel gave him the pearls from
the wicked witch's house. They were
able to buy lots of food with
the pearls, and they
all lived happily
ever after.

True or false?

Now that you have read the story, can you answer these true or false questions correctly?

1. Hansel and Gretel's father was a wizard.
True or false?

2. The **wicked witch**'s cottage was made of gold.
True or false?

3. At the end of the story Hansel and Gretel found their way home.
True or false?

4. Hansel and Gretel bought a horse with the pearls they found in the cottage.
True or false?

5. Hansel left a trail of swe to find the way home.
True or false?

Who's who?

Based on what they are saying, can you guess which character from the story each speech bubble belongs to?

"I lived in a gingerbread house in the middle of the woods. Who am I?"

"We ate the trail of breadcrumbs! Who are we?"

"I tricked the **wicked witch** with a chicken bone. Who am I?"

"I pushed the **wicked witch** into the oven. Who am I?"

"I said we should take Hansel and Gretel deeper into the woods. Who am I?"

"I was so pleased when Hansel and Gretel came home. Who am I?"